Please return/renew this item by the
last date shown to avoid a charge.
Books may also be renewed by phone
and Internet. May not be renewed if
required by another reader.

BARNET
LONDON BOROUGH
www.libraries.barnet.gov.uk

ANTHONY HOROWITZ

THE POWER OF FIVE: BOOK ONE

RAVEN'S GATE

THE GRAPHIC NOVEL

adapted by TONY LEE

illustrated by
DOM REARDON &
LEE O'CONNOR

WALKER
BOOKS

First published 2010 by Walker Books Ltd
87 Vauxhall Walk, London SE11 5HJ

10 9 8 7 6 5 4 3 2 1

Text and illustrations © 2010 Walker Books Ltd

Based on the original novel *Raven's Gate*
© 1983, 2005 Anthony Horowitz

Anthony Horowitz has asserted his moral rights.

This book has been typeset in CC Dave Gibbons

Printed and bound in Italy

British Library Cataloguing in Publication Data:
a catalogue record for this book is available from the
British Library

ISBN 978-1-4063-0647-7

www.walker.co.uk

www.powerof5.co.uk

Before the beginning
was the gate
And five gatekeepers

children

Four boys. One girl.

it has been written

The night of everlasting
darkness is drawing in.

The gate is about to open.
The gatekeepers must return.

"SO, WHERE IS HE?"

"HER NAME IS *JAYNE DEVERILL* -"

"- AND SHE SHOULD BE HERE ANY MINUTE NOW."

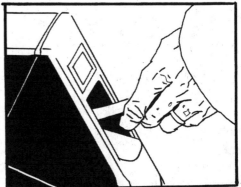

"NOWHERE!"

GREATER MALLING.

THREE HOURS TO KILL UNTIL THE NEXT BUS...

MAYBE I CAN WORK OUT WHAT'S GOING ON AROUND HERE.

Library

Reference

THERE HAS TO BE *SOMETHING* THAT CAN HELP ME.

"RAMBLES AROUND GREATER MALLING" BY ELIZABETH ASHWOOD.

CHAPTER SIX - RAVEN'S ... *GATE*.

YOU'RE *KIDDING* ME. SOMEONE REMOVED THE WHOLE CHAPTER!

Chapter 7

EXCUSE ME, I NEED TO USE THE INTERNET FOR A SCHOOL PROJECT, TO FIND OUT SOMETHING ABOUT RAVEN'S GATE.

NEVER HEARD OF IT.

NOR HAVE I - THAT'S WHY I WANT TO GO ON THE INTERNET.

"AT SOME TIME IN THE MIDDLE AGES, IT WAS DELIBERATELY TAKEN DOWN AND SMASHED."

"MORE THAN THAT - EACH STONE WAS GROUND TO POWDER."

"AND THEN THE POWDER WAS LOADED INTO CARTS AND CARRIED TO THE FOUR CORNERS OF BRITAIN - NORTH, SOUTH, EAST, WEST..."

"...AND THEN POURED INTO THE SEA. IT WAS NEVER MENTIONED AGAIN - IT WAS LIKE IT NEVER EXISTED."

"THE STONES WERE DESTROYED - BUT NOT THE GATE."

CLINK

"AND THE OLD ONES WERE NOT DEAD - JUST WAITING..."

SO HOW DID YOU HEAR OF IT?

THERE HAVE BEEN SOME WRITTEN RECORDS. THE DIARY OF A SPANISH MONK. CARVINGS ON A TEMPLE.

AND HOW DID I HEAR OF IT? I BELONG TO THE NEXUS. TWELVE OF US, INCLUDING SUSAN ASHWOOD.

THE WHOLE PURPOSE OF THE NEXUS - THE REASON IT EXISTS - IS TO HELP YOU WITH WHAT YOU MUST DO.

END OF BOOK ONE

ANTHONY HOROWITZ is one of the most popular contemporary children's writers. Both The Power of Five and Alex Rider are number one bestselling series enjoyed by millions of readers worldwide.

When Anthony launched the Alex Rider series in 2000, he created a phenomenon in children's books, spurring a new trend of junior spy books and inspiring thousands of previously reluctant readers. Hailed as a reading hero, Anthony has also won many major awards including The Bookseller Association/Nielsen Author of the Year Award, the Children's Book of the Year Award at the British Book Awards, and the Red House Children's Book Award. The first Alex Rider adventure, STORMBREAKER, was made into a blockbuster movie in 2006.

Anthony's other titles for Walker Books include the Diamond Brothers mysteries; GROOSHAM GRANGE and its sequel, RETURN TO GROOSHAM GRANGE; THE DEVIL AND HIS BOY, GRANNY, THE SWITCH, and a new collection of horror stories, MORE BLOODY HOROWITZ. Anthony also writes extensively for TV, with programmes including FOYLE'S WAR, MIDSOMER MURDERS, POIROT, and most recently COLLISION. He is married to television producer Jill Green and lives in London with his sons, Nicholas and Cassian, and their dog, Limpy.

You can find out more about Anthony and his books at:
www.anthonyhorowitz.com
www.alexrider.com
www.powerof5.co.uk